A Guess the Expressions Book

Annie and the
SECRET
LANGUAGE
OF FACES

written by
ANNIE SÄRNBLAD

illustrated by
SARAH MATTERN

Illustrations and Book Design by Sarah Mattern (sarahmattern.com)

ISBN 979-8-9883819-4-5

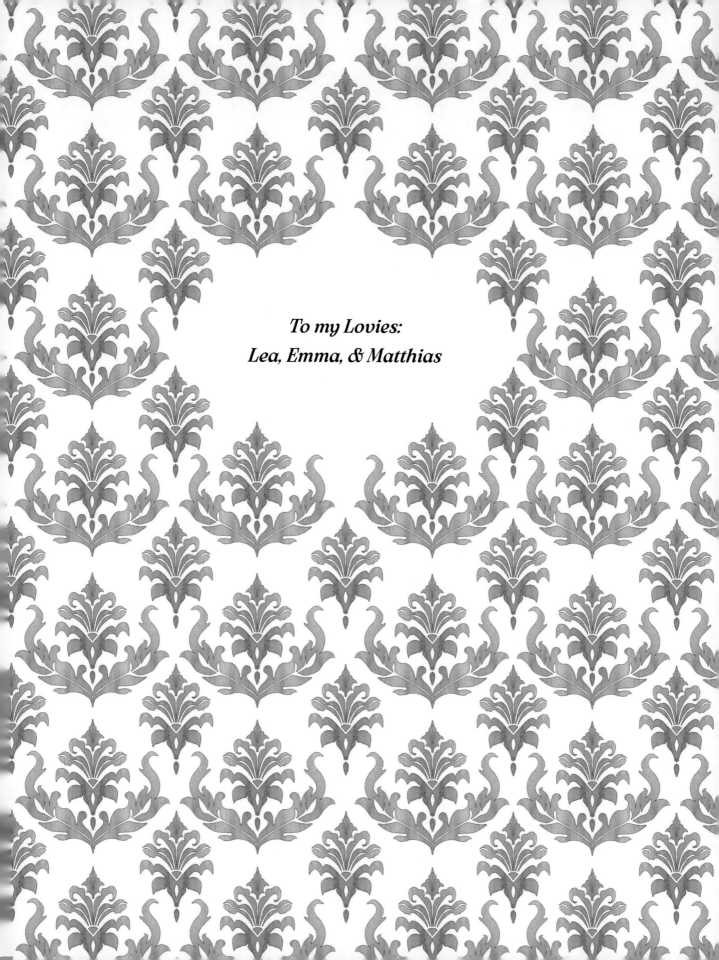

To my Lovies:
Lea, Emma, & Matthias

Once there was a little girl named Annie who knew the secret language of faces. She could see every emotion in people's facial expressions. Even when they tried to hide what they were feeling.

She could see if people were sad or angry ... even if they were just a teeny bit sad or a teeny bit angry. And even if no one else noticed or cared.

Annie knew that people's hearts grow lonely if their feelings aren't seen.

The expressions on people's faces showed Annie who was loving and who was cruel. She could also see who was struggling and who was hurting.

This ability helped her be kind when her friends needed extra care. It also helped keep her safe when the grown ups around her were angry at their problems.

The truth is that most babies are born knowing the secret language of faces. But, as they learn mouth words, the face language slips away into a box in the sleeping corners of their brains.

Over time, the box becomes locked and hidden.

Most big children have forgotten that there was a box stored in their brains at all. The space that used to belong to all the baby pieces of life gets filled up with words and thinking.

Annie held onto her language of faces as she grew older because the people in her family were often angry. She kept her knowledge of faces and emotions close to her heart for protection.

There are some magical babies who rarely use words. They keep the secret language and are able to see other people's feelings on their faces.

Annie had a friend named Thomas who was this way. He kept his secret language of faces as he grew up because he still needed it. Sometimes he made big expressions and hoped that others could tell what he was feeling.

Thomas could read on Annie's face that she loved him. In turn, he would offer her a warm, loving smile. She always knew this was his gift to her.

Annie often thought that Thomas knew far more than most grown ups.

When Annie told the adults around her about the secret language of faces, they didn't believe her. It seemed that no one else could see what she could see.

So Annie built a boat and sailed away, over the salty sea, to look for people who would be kind and keep her safe.

When Annie reached a far-away shore, she found she didn't understand the new people's words.

So she put her English away to give the new language space to grow inside her brain.

Hmm, maybe...

Eww, gross.

Soon, Annie found that she could understand the new people by watching their facial expressions. Little by little, she used these expressions to puzzle together and figure out what the new words meant.

So exciting!

Then Annie did the same thing again and again. She traveled to new lands with new languages. She learned new spoken words by reading the expressions and feelings on people's faces.

She also discovered that expressions for feelings were the same on every person in every land. No matter how young the face, no matter how old the face. No matter the shapes of the eyes or nose or chin. No matter the beautiful shades of skin across lands and cultures.

In one of the lands, Annie stayed and grew up. She fell in love and soon had a family of her own. When her three children were little, she knew she wanted to help them hold onto the secret language of faces.

So her children would feel loved and understood.

So they could see if people needed help and be kind.

So they would know if people were angry or dangerous.

Love Smile

Before her children lost their connection to the secret language, Annie practiced making faces with them. Her babies copied her expressions, mirroring their mama's face. As they played this game, Annie described each expression with her own simple words.

As her little ones grew, they helped her think up fun, clear words for the expressions too.

Turn the page to see a few!

Kindness

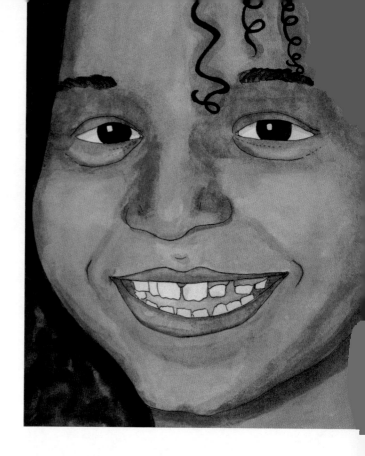

GUESS THE EXPRESSIONS!

What emotions do you see on these faces? Make a guess and turn the page to see if you got it right!

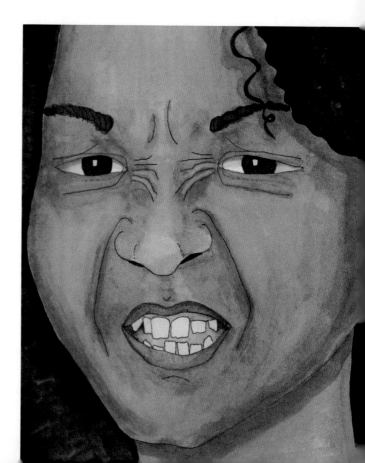

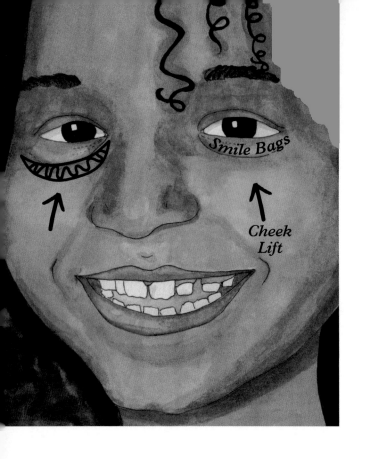

Happy Face

Smile bags stick out when the cheeks pop up in a real smile. Smile bags are the bumps under the eyes that have shadows below. Showing true happiness makes people around you happy too!

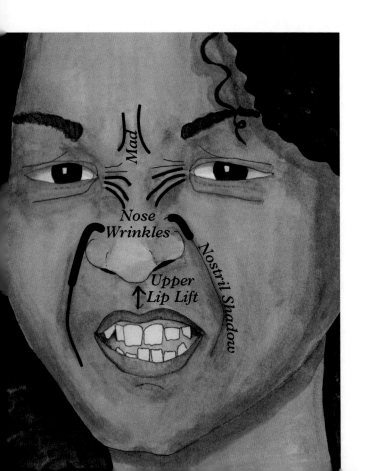

No Face

Nose wrinkles and nostril shadows show on the No Face. This is the "Ew, I don't want to" face. The tiny expression of the No Face looks like a bunny rabbit twitching its nose. The bunny says, "No! Yuck!"

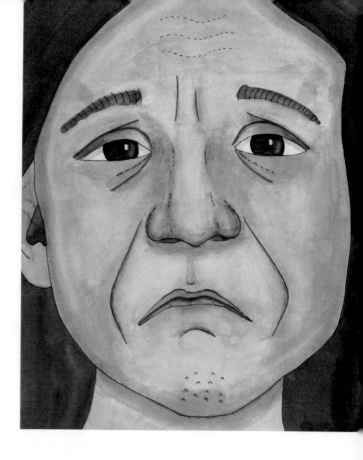

GUESS THE EXPRESSIONS!

What emotions do
you see on these faces?
Make a guess and
turn the page to see
if you got it right!

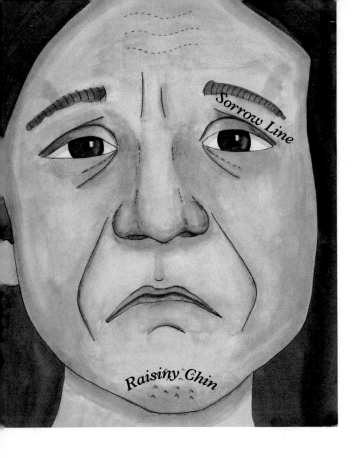

Sadness

Sadness shows on our faces in sorrow lines and a puckered chin. Sorrow lines are slanted lines made in the skin below our eyebrows. A puckered chin squeezes the part of our chin that is smooth like a grape into a dimpled raisin.

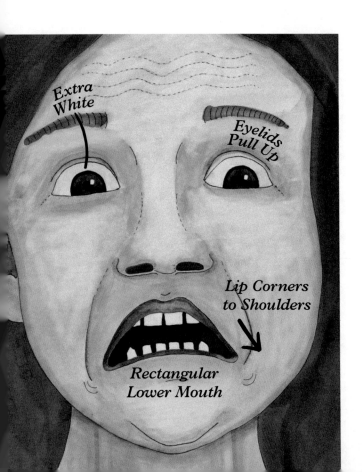

Fear

When we're scared, our eyebrows pull straight up, and our eyelids pull way back so we can easily see how to escape a scary situation. The lower mouth makes a rectangle shape, opening our mouths wide so we can yell for help.

GUESS THE EXPRESSIONS!

What emotions do you see on these faces? Make a guess and turn the page to see if you got it right!

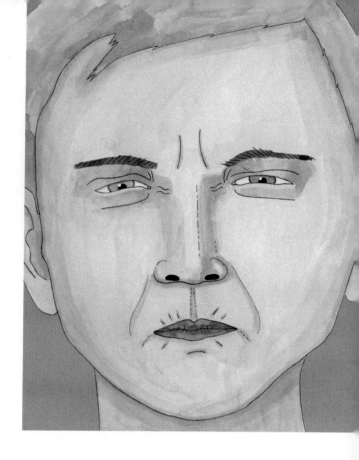

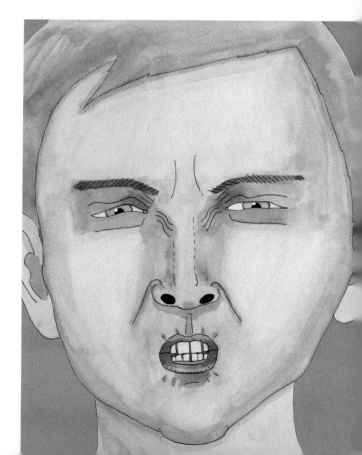

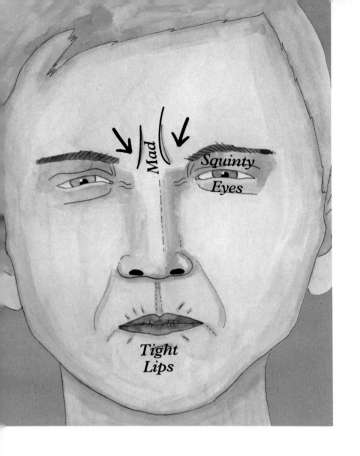

Anger

Anger shows on the face in squinty eyes, a furrowed brow, and a tight mouth. Sometimes people who are thinking hard look angry because they furrow their brows. Remember, if they are angry, their lips will always be tight.

• • • • • • • • • • • • • • • • • • • •

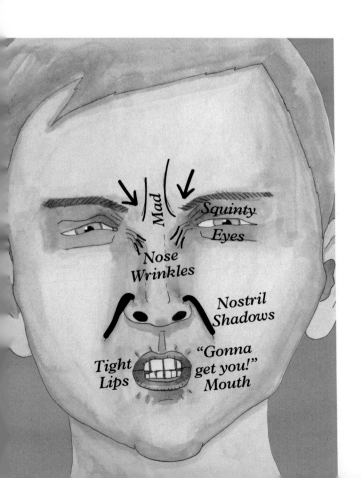

RUN! Face

The RUN! Face shows extreme anger with a furrowed brow, wrinkly nose, nostril shadows, and a "Gonna get you!" mouth. It looks like the growl of an animal that wants to bite you. If you see this face, make sure to run and tell a safe grown up!

GUESS THE EXPRESSIONS!

What emotions do
you see on these faces?
Make a guess and
turn the page to see
if you got it right!

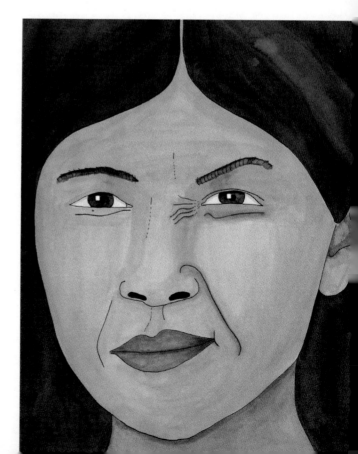

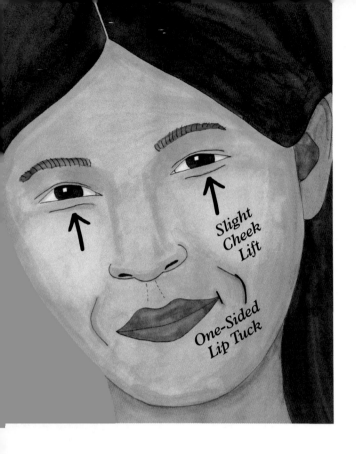

Slight Cheek Lift

One-Sided Lip Tuck

Knowing Smile

A knowing smile tucks one side of the mouth into the cheek. It means, "I know something that I haven't told you yet." In this picture, the girl's expression is kind because her cheeks are lifted.

• •

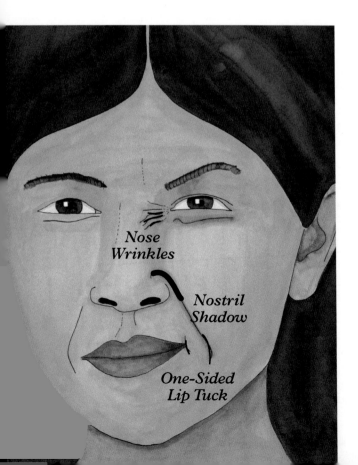

Nose Wrinkles

Nostril Shadow

One-Sided Lip Tuck

Mean Knowing Smile

A mean knowing smile tucks one side of the mouth into the cheek and shows a nostril shadow of disgust. It means, "I know something that will hurt you." This is also called contempt. Tell a safe grown up if you see this expression.

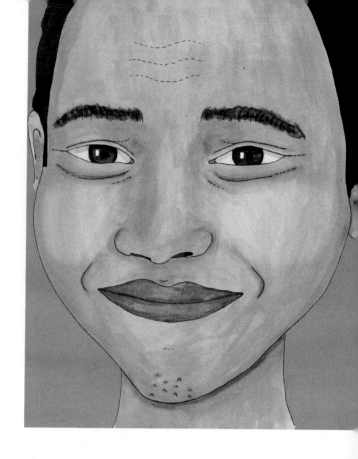

GUESS THE EXPRESSIONS!

What emotions do you see on these faces? Make a guess and turn the page to see if you got it right!

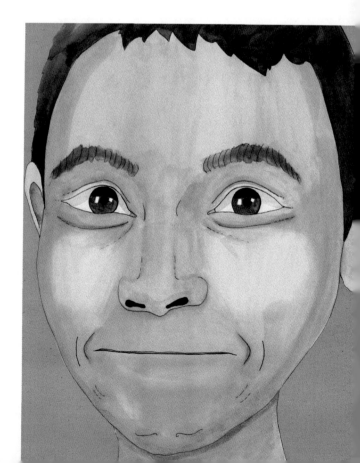

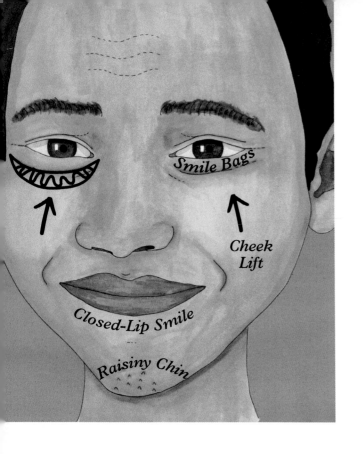

Kindness, Empathy

In kindness and empathy, the lips stay closed, the cheeks rise high to make smile bags under the eyes, and the chin puckers and looks raisiny. This face says, "I feel your sad feelings and hope things get better."

● ● ● ● ● ● ● ● ● ● ● ● ● ● ● ● ●

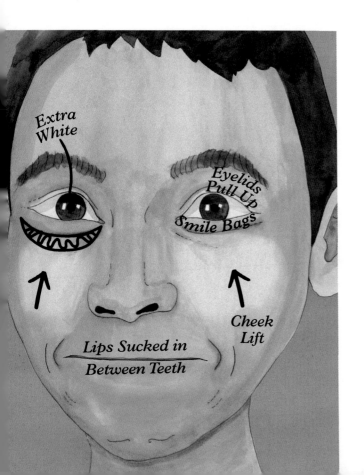

Mischief

In mischief, the cheeks lift, and smile bags push out under the eyes. The eyelids pull up, and the lips pull in like you're holding back laughter.

PRACTICE THE FACES!

Happy Face 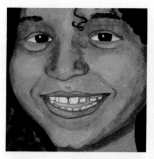  No Face

Sadness   Fear

Anger 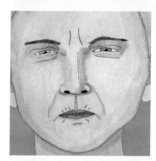 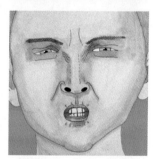 RUN! Face

Knowing
Smile   Mean
Knowing
Smile

Kindness,
Empathy   Mischief

Annie taught her little ones that when people tell the truth, their expressions match what they say. When they tell a lie, their expressions don't match their words.

"It's ok to say, *I don't like potatoes*," she told her children, "if indeed you don't like potatoes. This is the No Face that matches those words."

"But if someone says, *I'm happy to see you*, which are nice words, but they make the No Face, then they aren't telling the truth. So come tell me what you see."

No Face

"The RUN! Face looks like this. If someone makes the RUN! Face, please run and come tell me. Lies and bad intentions are not safe and should not be around children. So come tell me, my loves, what you see."

The RUN! Face

"I will slay dragons with you. Together we are fierce and strong. Together we will keep you safe.

"If face feelings and mouth words don't match, come tell me. If someone makes the RUN! Face, come tell me.

"Tell me my loves, come tell me!

"My wish for you is to:
be kind,
be kind,
be kind.
Except if it's a choice between being kind and staying safe, then we ALWAYS choose safe."

"What's the face you make when you look at us mama?"
Her little ones asked.

"That's my love smile, it's a bit softer and more tender
than my happy smile, but both give me smile bags under
my eyes. The shadows under smile bags are like crescent
moons on their sides. The love smile also has a soft lift of
the cheeks and a closed mouth with just the corners of
the lips lifting."

"Mama, what about that one that you make, the halfsy
smile?"

"Ah, that's my knowing smile—like the Mona Lisa
woman I showed you in the painting. The knowing smile
means, *I know something I have not yet told you.*"

*Knowing
Smile*
*(with a little
extra love)*

"Do you know, my loves, what turns a knowing smile into a mean knowing smile?" Annie asked her little ones.

"Ohhh, I know!" said her eldest. "When there's a nostril shadow, the knowing smile is unkind. Then it means, *I know something that can hurt you!*"

"Yes! And it's especially dangerous when that mean face comes with nice words. Think of the wicked witch with the poison apple. When the words don't match the face, run quickly and come tell me."

"We will mama, we will!" They said. And they always did.

Mean Knowing Smile

As Annie's children grew up, it was time for them to set sail on their own adventures.

Before they left, Annie told them about the good, safe, helping people of the world. "There are so many of us," she told them. "Sometimes we hide in plain sight. It's important to find us. Our faces and hearts can speak to each other even without words."

"Look for the people who always show empathy and kindness on their faces when someone else is hurt," she told them. "Look for the people who tell the truth, whose expressions match their words. People who care about keeping other people safe can be trusted."

Annie wanted to help more people see each other's true hearts and feelings. She knew that reading facial expressions is the deepest of listening skills.

So she set off to teach the world the secret language of faces. And teach she did. Old people and young people, people in her own city and people far away. And as she did, she reminded everyone she met to look around and spread kindness wherever it is most needed.

When we see other people well, we are better able to help, to include, to love, and to protect each other.

We humans need to be seen to feel loved.

Made in the USA
Coppell, TX
27 October 2024

39217475R00024